EASY KEYBOARD BUMPER BOOK
EASY MUSIC FOR ALL KEYBOARDS
BY ROGER EVANS

100 GREAT TUNES
TO PLAY AND ENJOY
ALL SPECIALLY ARRANGED
FOR KEYBOARDS BY ROGER EVANS

Beryl   8   And I love you so
Val   96   Mandy
Gwen   8   And I love you so

© International Music Publications Ltd
First published in 1989 by International Music Publications Ltd
International Music Publications Ltd is a Faber Music company
Bloomsbury House 74–77 Great Russell Street London WC1B 3DA
Printed in England by Caligraving Ltd
All rights reserved

ISBN10: 0-571-53026-5
EAN13: 978-0-571-53026-7

To buy Faber Music publications or to find out about the full range of titles available,
please contact your local music retailer or Faber Music sales enquiries:

Faber Music Ltd, Burnt Mill, Elizabeth Way, Harlow, CM20 2HX England
Tel: +44(0)1279 82 89 82   Fax: +44(0)1279 82 89 83
sales@fabermusic.com   fabermusic.com

EASY KEYBOARD BUMPER BOOK
EASY MUSIC FOR ALL KEYBOARDS
BY ROGER EVANS

Easy music for all keyboards

All music specially arranged for keyboards by Roger Evans

Introduction

Welcome to the Easy Keyboard Bumper Book.

This collection of 100 tunes has been specially chosen to give you a broad variety of good-sounding music to play on your keyboard. Here you will find classic pop songs, love songs, easy rock music, motown classics, theme songs from great films, show tunes, tunes which have become jazz classics, tunes with latin and calypso rhythms — and more.

Each tune has been chosen because it sounds good on modern keyboards — and all music is specially arranged to be easy and enjoyable to play. All tunes are in easy keys and have easy chords.

This music is perfect for everyone who learned to play with the Playing Keyboards book and cassette. It is also ideal for everyone who wants to play good music easily on modern keyboard instruments.

Playing Hints

The music in this book follows the same easy style used in the *Playing Keyboards* books:

Suggested Voices and Rhythms are given at the beginning of every tune, like this:

> Organ / Flute
> Ballad / Pops or Rock (Medium)

You can choose whichever settings suit your keyboard. Here, you could choose either the Organ or Flute voice, and set a Ballad, Pops or Rock rhythm.

The suggested Tempo (speed) of the music is given in brackets like this: (Medium). Adjust the Tempo control on your keyboard to this suggested setting before you begin each tune. (If you like, set the Tempo slower than suggested until you are comfortable playing a new tune).

If your keyboard does not have any of the suggested voices or rhythms, choose voices and rhythms which suit the music you are playing.

Special Effects which you can add to the music are shown in brackets over some tunes:

(Arpeggio/Variation) — means you can add an automatic 'Arpeggio' to the backing of a tune if your keyboard has this effect; or you can use an auto chord accompaniment 'variation' which gives a 'rippling' effect.

Fingering — Finger numbers are shown in front of notes where the fingering is not obvious, and where the fingers need to move to different keys:

1 = thumb   2 = index finger   3 = middle finger   4 = ring finger   5 = little finger

Chords — You can play all of the music in this book with easy 'One Finger Chords', 'Casio Chords' or 'Single Finger Chords' — or you can use 'Fingered Chords'.

Chord symbols are shown over the music wherever a chord change is needed. Chords shown in brackets are optional, and may be left out for easy playing:

C(7) — means you can play a C7 chord, or a C chord.

(C7) — means this chord is not essential and may be left out if necessary.

All of the tunes are easier to play if the optional chords are left out. However, you will find the music usually sounds far better if *all* chords are played, so try and play them all if you can.

'Transposing' — Many keyboards have a very useful facility called a 'Transposer' which changes the pitch of the instrument. This is very helpful for music which is too high or too low for singing, and the 'Transposer' can also be used when you play along with certain other musical instruments, and for special effects.

For singing — If the music is too high for the singer, try setting the Transposer to B♭ (♭2 or -2). If the music is still too high, try setting it to G (♭5 or -5).

If the music is too low for the singer, try setting the Transposer to E♭ (#3 or +3) or F (#5 or +5).

Playing With Other Instruments — If you have friends who play B♭ instruments like the clarinet, trumpet or tenor saxophone, and you would them to play along with you, *and read your music,* set the Transposer to B♭ (♭2 or -2). For E♭ instruments set the Transposer to E♭ (#3 or +3).

(There is no need to use the Transposer when you play along with a guitar, flute, violin, recorder or most other instruments — as long as they 'tune' to your keyboard.)

You can also use the Transposer to give music a 'lift'. Try playing a tune through once. Then, without stopping, set the Transposer to C# (#1 or +1), D (#2 or +2) or higher — and play the tune again. (As with all special effects, it is best not to over-use this trick!)

Always remember to re-set the Transposer to C (0) when you have finished.

You can find more playing hints, easy-to-follow instruction and more good tunes in the *Playing Keyboards* book and songbooks, which are obtainable from your music dealer.

Wishing you many happy hours playing the music in this book.

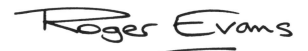

Alone

Words and Music by
BILLY STEINBERG and TOM KELLY

Trumpet/Brass or Jazz Organ/Organ 2
Rock or Ballad/Pops (Medium-Slow)
(Add Arpeggio/Variation)

I hear the tick-ing of the clock; I'm ly-ing here, the
You don't know how long I have wanted to touch your lips and

room's pitch dark.—
hold you tight.—

I won-der where you are to - night, no an-swer on your
You don't know how long I have waited and I was gon-na

tel - e - phone.—— And the
tell you to-night.— But the

night goes by so ve-ry slow, Oh,— I
sec-ret is still my own, and— my

hope that it won't end—— though,⟩
love for you is still un-known,⟩ A -

lone.

'til now —— I al - ways got by —— on my

own, I nev - er real -ly cared un - til I met you.

And now it chills me to the bone.

How do I get —— you a - lone?

1.

How do I get— you a - lone?

2.

lone, a - lone, ——————— a -

lone?——————

Instrumental*

*The instrumental is optional and may be left out if you wish.

And I Love You So

Words and Music
by DON McLEAN

Violin/Strings 5 0
Ballad/Pops (Medium) 25
Tempo 72

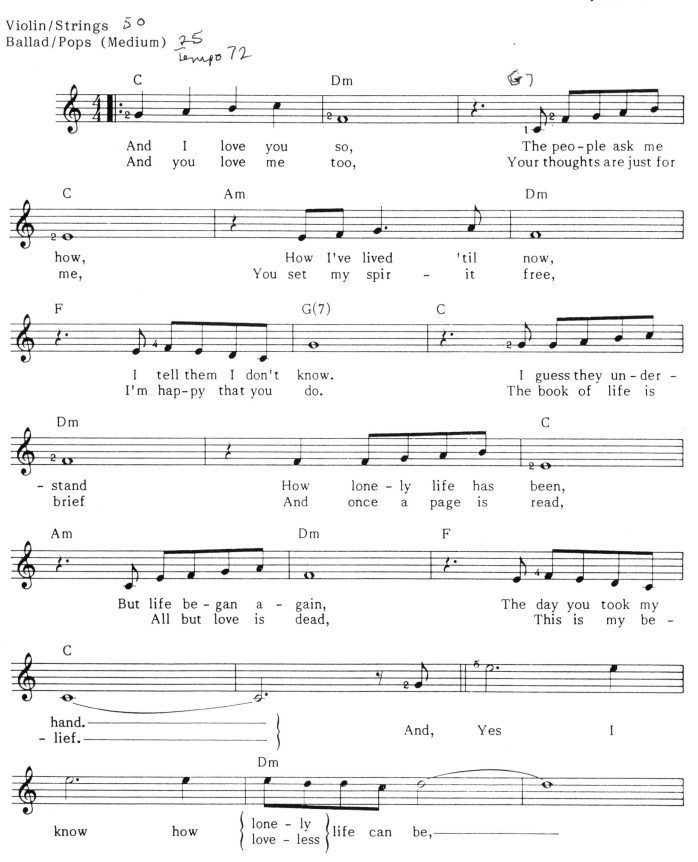

And I love you so,   The peo-ple ask me
And you love me too,   Your thoughts are just for

how,   How I've lived   'til   now,
me,   You set my spir - it   free,

I tell them I don't know.   I guess they un - der -
I'm hap-py that you   do.   The book of life is

- stand   How lone - ly life has been,
brief   And once a page is   read,

But life be - gan a - gain,   The day you took my
All but love is dead,   This is my be -

hand.   And,   Yes   I
- lief.

know   how { lone - ly } life can be,
          { love - less }

Arthur's Theme (Best That You Can Do)

Words and Music
by BURT BACHARACH, CAROLE BAYER SAGER,
CHRISTOPHER CROSS and PETER ALLEN

Trumpet/Brass

Ballad/Pops or Bossa Nova (Medium)

what-'ve I found?
want him to be.

Instrumental

When you get caught be-tween the moon and New York
Ci — ty.

I know it's cra - zy,

but it's true.

If you get caught be-tween the moon and New York
Ci — ty, the best that you can do,

the best that you can do

is fall— in love.

Baker Street

Words and Music
by GERRY RAFFERTY

Saxophone/Trombone or Jazz Organ
8-beat or Rock (Medium)

INTRO (Optional) Play instrumental on next page.

Verse: Wind-ing your way down on Bak - er Street,
This city des - ert makes you feel so cold. He's got

light in your head and —— dead on your feet. Well, an -
so many peo - ple but he's got no soul. And it's

- oth - er cra - zy day you'll drink the night a - way and for -
tak - ing so long —— to find out you were wrong when you

- get a - bout ev - 'ry - thing.
thought it held ev - 'ry - thing.

Chorus: You used to think that it was so ea - sy.
An - oth - er year and then you'll be hap - py.

You used to see that it was so ea - sy, But you're try - in',
Just one more year and then you'll be hap - py, But you're cry - in',

1. you're try - in' now.
2. you're cry - in' now.

INSTRUMENTAL (& Intro)

Verse 2.   Way down the street there's a lot in his place
He opens his door he's got that look on his face
And he asks you where you've been
You tell him who you've seen and you talk about anything.

He's got this dream about buyin' some land, he's gonna
Give up the booze and the one night stands and
Then you'll settle down with some quiet little town
And forget about everything.

Chorus 2.   But you know you'll always keep movin'
You know he's never gonna stop movin'
'Cause he's rollin', he's the rollin' stone.

When you wake up it's a new mornin';
The sun is shinin', it's a new mornin'
And you're goin', you're goin' home.

Ben

Words by DON BLACK
Music by WALTER SCHARF

Flute or Violin
Ballad/Pops (Medium-Slow)

Blueberry Hill

Words and Music by
AL LEWIS, LARRY STOCK
and VINCENT ROSE

Jazz Organ/Organ 2 or Trumpet
Slow Rock (Medium)

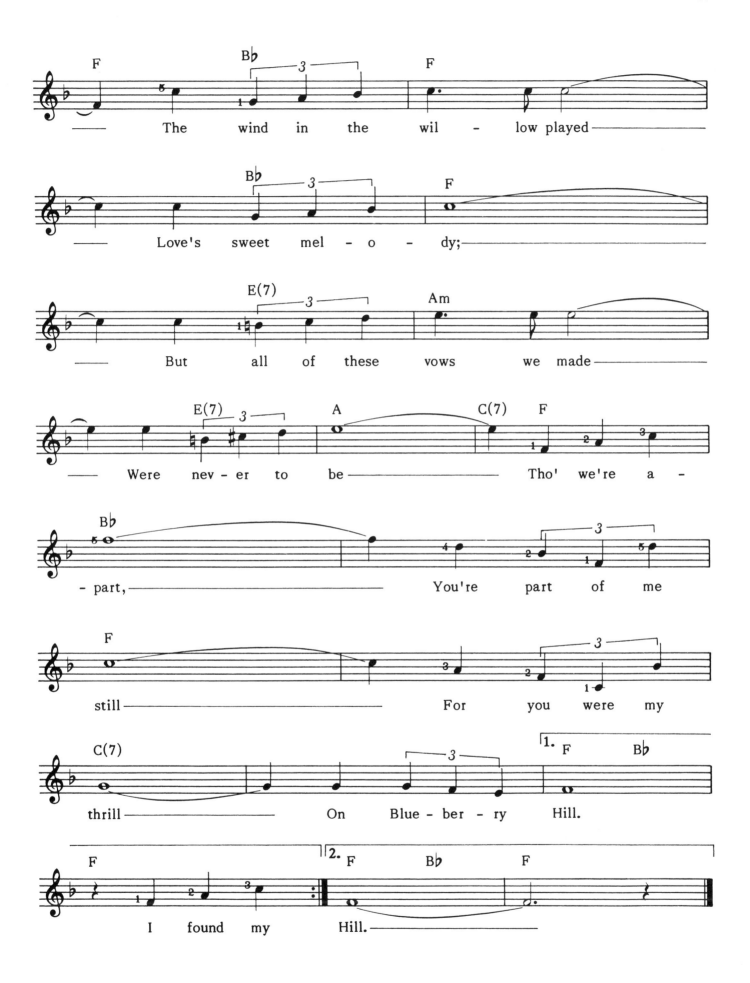

Breaking Up Is Hard To Do

Words and Music by
NEIL SEDAKA and HOWARD GREENFIELD

Violin/Strings or Jazz Organ
Regular version: Ballad/Pops or Rock (Medium-Fast)
Slow version: Ballad/Pops

Don't take your love ——————— a -

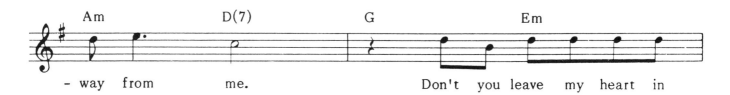

- way from me. Don't you leave my heart in

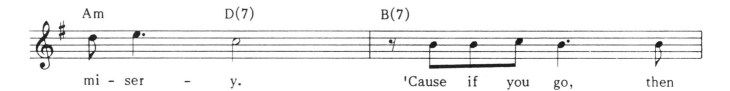

mi - ser - y. 'Cause if you go, then

I'll be blue, —— break - in' up is hard to

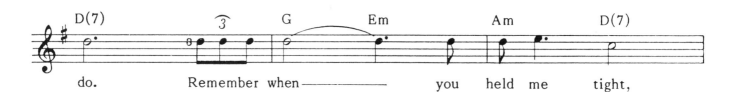

do. Remember when———— you held me tight,

and you kiss - ed me all through the night.

Think of all that we've been through—— And

By The Time I Get To Phoenix

Words and Music by JIM WEBB

Trombone/Trumpet or Jazz Organ
Ballad/Pops (Medium-Slow)

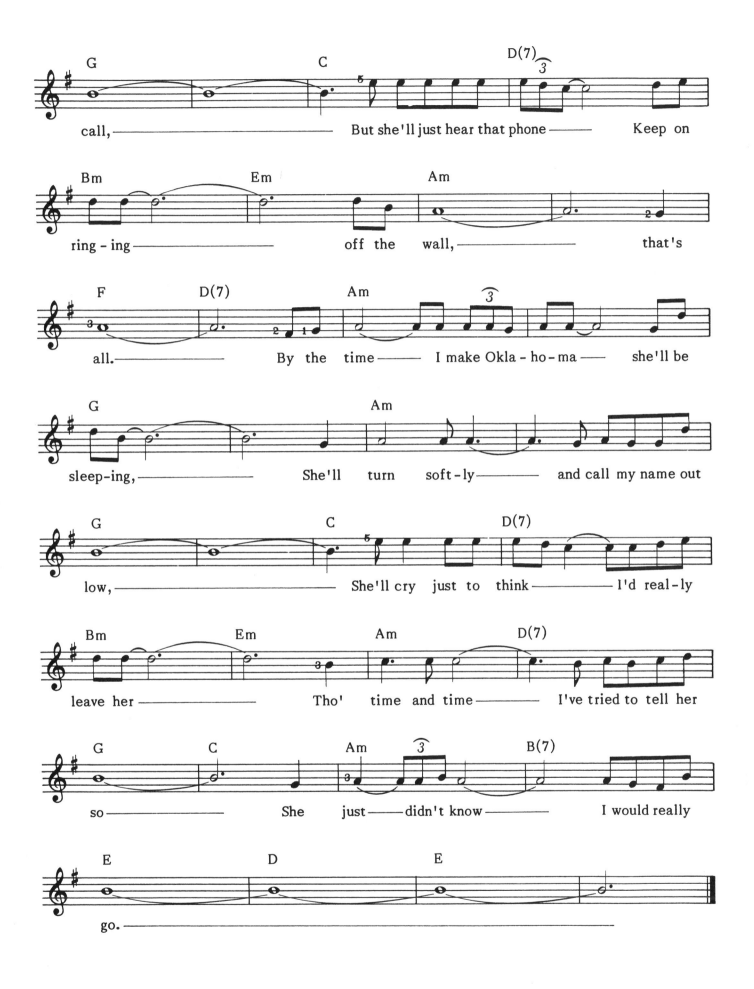

Can't Help Falling In Love

Words and Music by GEORGE WEISS,
HUGH PERETTI and LUIGI CREATORE

Organ/Organ 1
Slow Rock or Ballad/Pops (Medium-Slow)
(Add Arpeggio/Variation)

Cavatina (Theme from 'The Deerhunter')

By STANLEY MYERS

Organ or Violin/Strings
Slow Rock (Medium–Slow) or Waltz (Slow)
(Add Arpeggio/Variation)

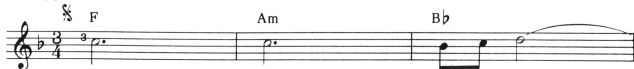

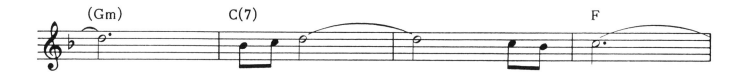

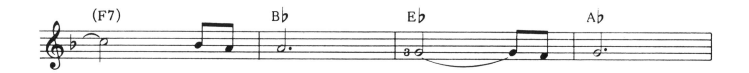

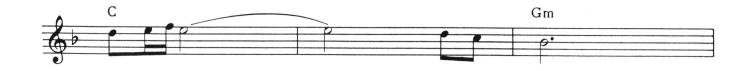

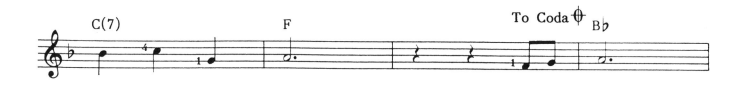

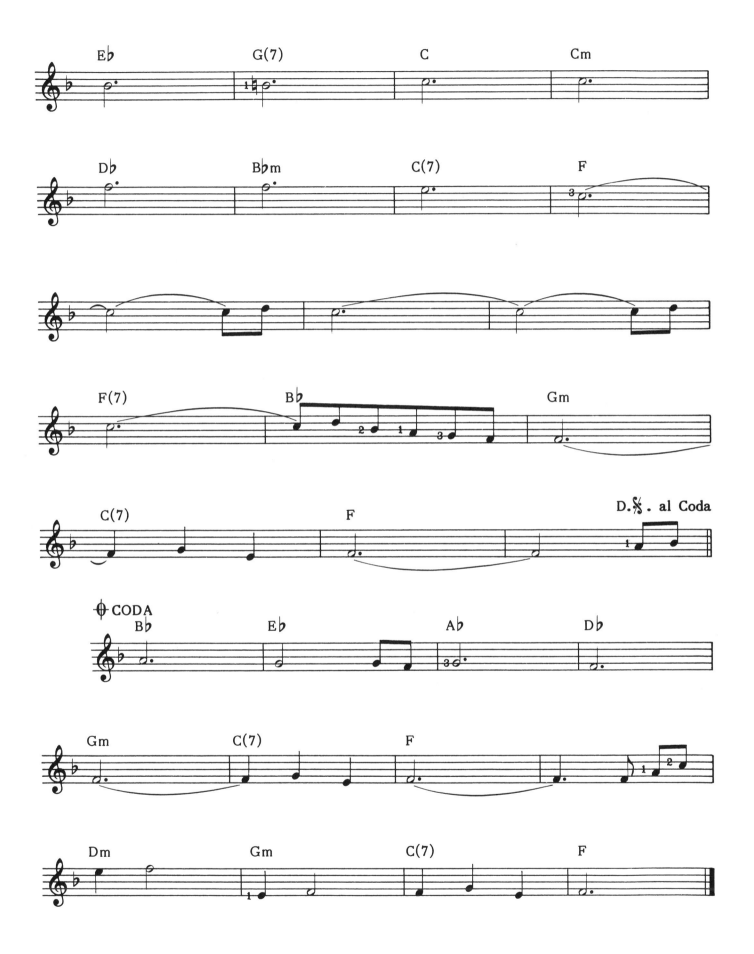

Chariots Of Fire

Composed by VANGELIS

Piano/Electric Piano or Guitar
Slow Rock (Medium-Slow)
(Add Stereo Chorus/Stereo Symphonic)

Warner Chappell Music Ltd, London W1Y 3FA

The Christmas Song
(Chestnuts Roasting On An Open Fire)

Words and Music by
MEL TORME and ROBERT WELLS

Accordion or Trombone/Trumpet
Ballad/Pops (Medium-Slow)

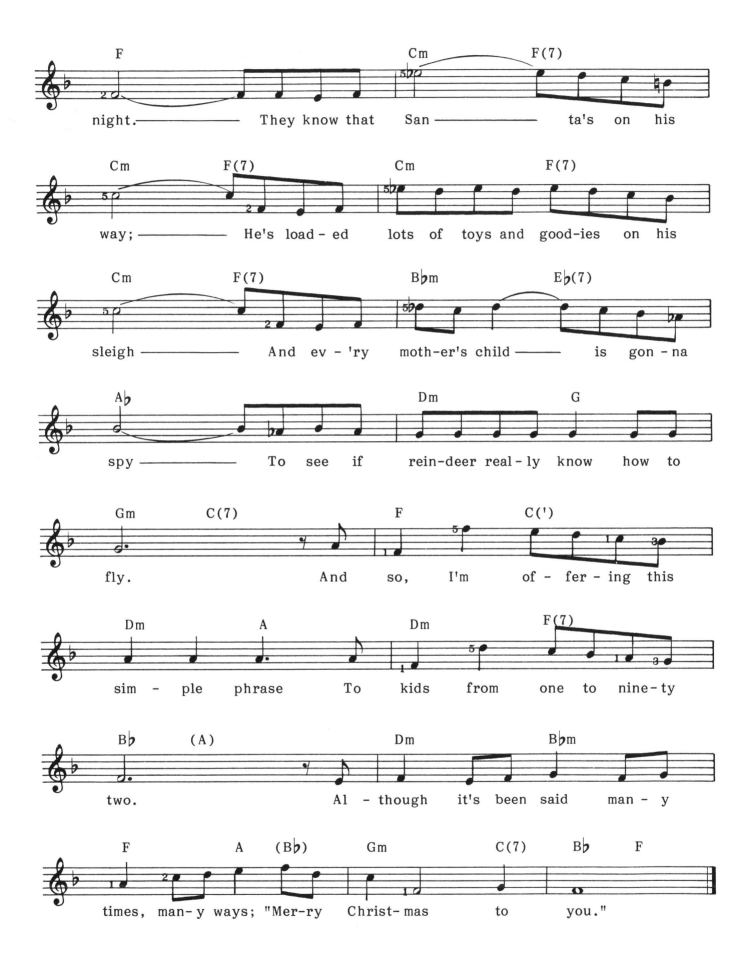

Close To You (They Long To Be)

Words by HAL DAVID
Music by BURT BACHARACH

Flute, Jazz Organ or Electric Piano
Ballad/Pops or Bossa Nova (Medium)

Country Gardens

Adapted and Arranged
by ROGER EVANS

Trumpet/Brass or Flute/Clarinet
Ballad/Pops or Slow Rock (Medium)
(Add Arpeggio/Variation)

Cry Me A River

Words and Music
by ARTHUR HAMILTON

Flute/Clarinet or Jazz Organ
Ballad/Pops (Medium-Slow)

Dancing In The Street

Words and Music by WILLIAM STEVENSON,
MARVIN GAYE and IVY HUNTER

Trumpet/Brass or Organ
Rock (Medium - Slow)

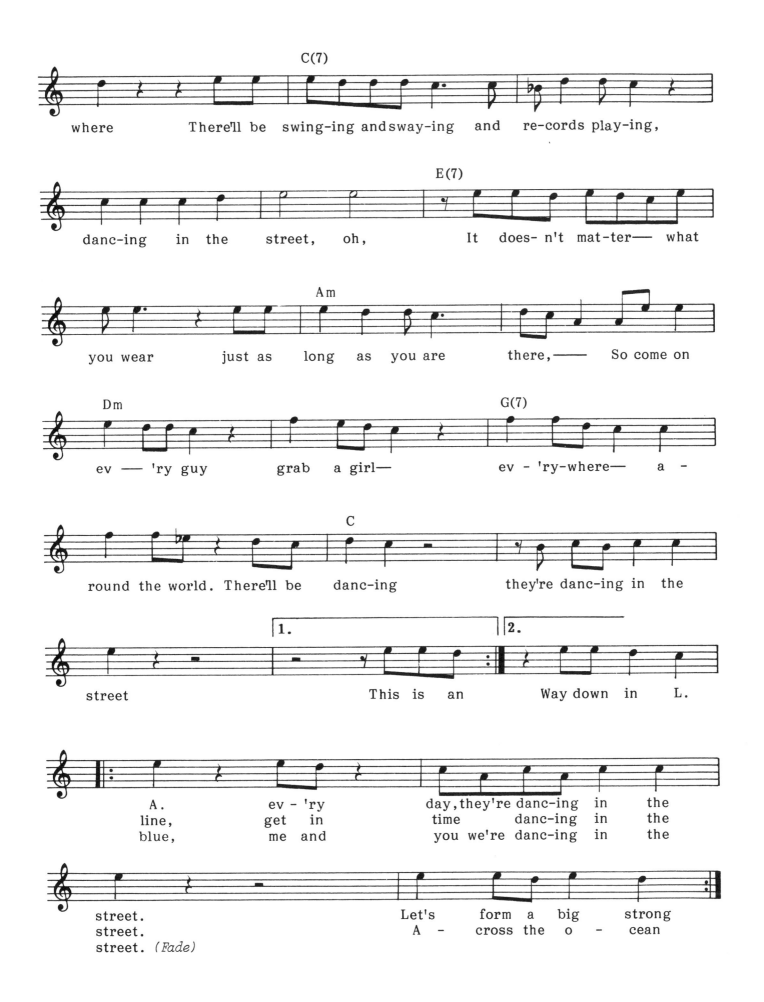

Dark Eyes

New Arrangement
by ROGER EVANS

Violin/Strings or Electric Guitar
Rock or March (Medium-Fast)

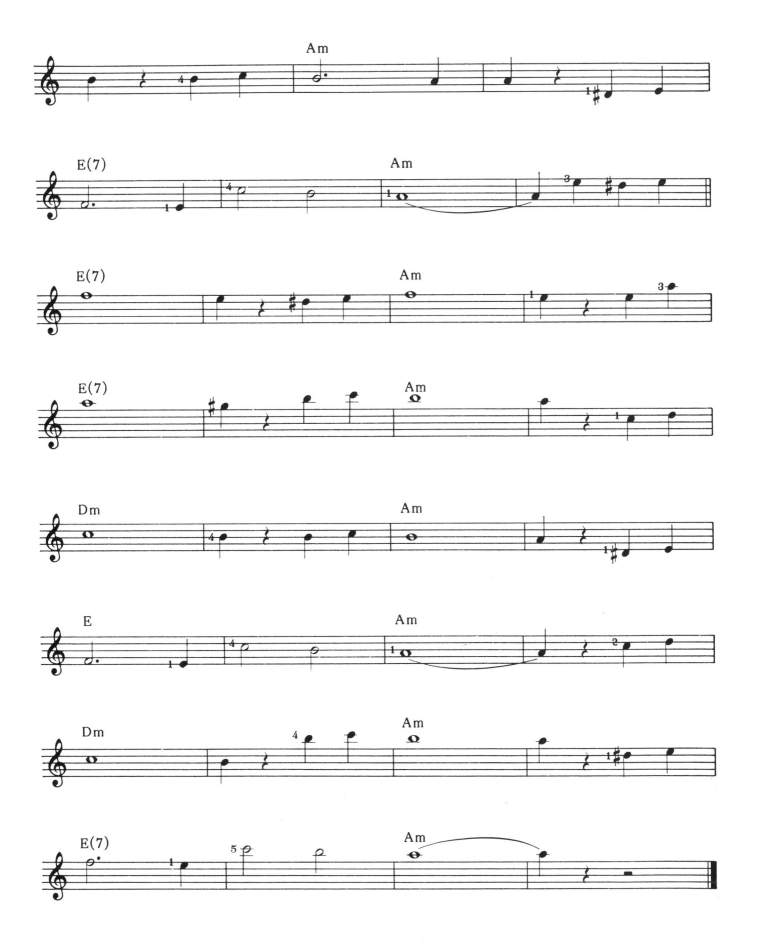

Do You Know Where You're Going To?
(Theme from 'Mahogany')

Words by GERRY GOFFIN
Music by MIKE MASSER

Organ or Violin/Strings
Ballad/Pops (Medium)
(Add Arpeggio/Variation)

The Dock Of The Bay (Sittin' On)

Words and Music by
STEVE CROPPER and OTIS REDDING

Jazz Organ or Electric Guitar
8-beat/Rock (Medium)

43

Look like —— noth —— ing gon-na change, ——

ev – 'ry – thing —————— still —— re-mains the same. ——

I can't do what ten peo-ple tell me to do

so I guess I'll re-main ———— the same. ——

⊕ CODA

(Whistle)

1.

2.

Verse 3. Sittin' here resting my bones, and the loneliness won't leave me alone.
Two thousand miles I roam just to make this dock my home
Now I'm just sittin' on the dock of the bay, watchin' the tide roll away
Just sittin' on the dock of the bay. Yes, the tide. **(To Coda)**

Easy

Words and Music
by LIONEL RICHIE

Violin/Strings or Clarinet
Ballad/Pops (Slow)

Know it sounds funny, but I just can't stand the pain;
Why in the world would an-y body put chains on me?

Girl, I'm leav-ing you to-mor-row———
I've paid my dues to make it———

Seems to me girl, you know I've done all I can;
Ev-'ry-body wants me to be what they want me to be;

You see, I begged, stole and I bor-rowed, Yeah———
I'm not hap-py when I try to fake it, No———

ooh, That's why I'm ea-sy, Ah——————— I'm ea-sy like Sun-day

morn-ing. Ah——————— That's why I'm ea-sy,———

——— I'm ea-sy like Sun-day morn——————— ing.

ing. I wan-na be high, so high: I wan-na be

free to know the things I do are right. I wan-na be

free, just me, Oh, babe.

That's why I'm

ea-sy, Ah I'm ea-sy like Sun-day

morn-ing, Ah That's why I'm

ea-sy, I'm ea-sy like Sun-day

morn ing.

Easy Lover

Words by PHIL COLLINS
Music by PHILIP BAILEY,
PHIL COLLINS and NATHAN EAST

Organ/Organ 1 or Electric Guitar
Rock (Medium-Fast)

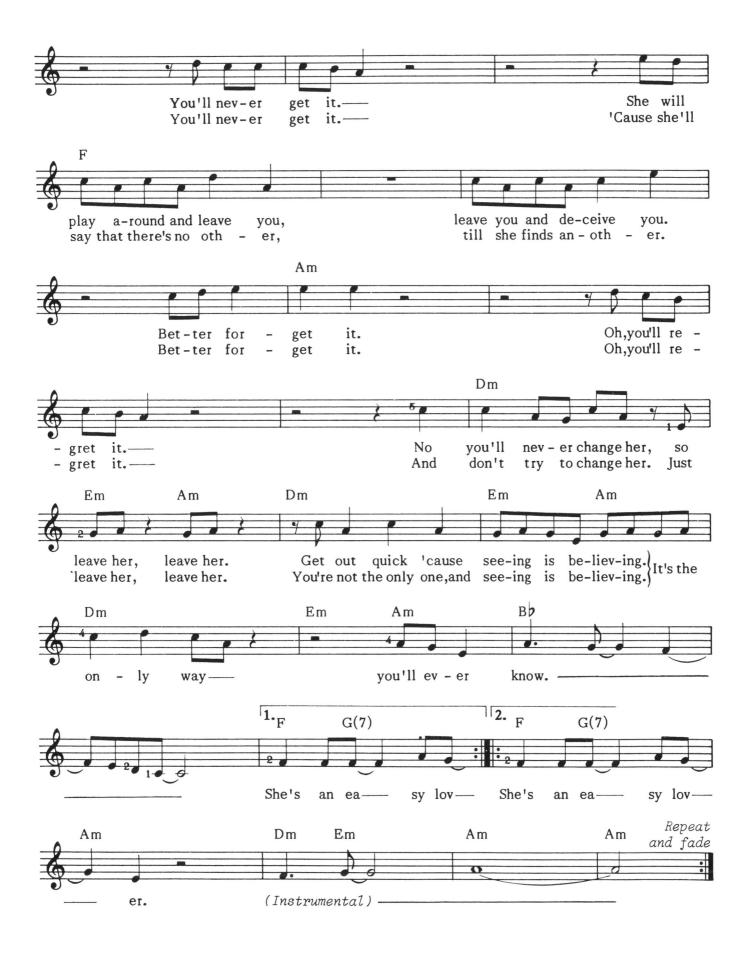

El Condor Pasa

Adapted and Arranged
by ROGER EVANS

Flute
March (Medium)

© 1989 International Music Publications, Woodford Green, Essex IG8 8HN

Endless Love

Words and Music
by LIONEL RICHIE

Jazz Organ or Trumpet
Ballad/Pops (Medium-Slow)

much   you —— care ——————   Oh ———— yes,   you will
world   to   me ———————————   Oh   I   know   I ——

al   -   ways   be   my   end - less
found   in   you   my   end - less

1. love.   2. love.   Oh, and——

CODA

And   yes ————————————   you'll   be   the

on - ly —— one ————————   Oh,   no   I can't de -

- ny   this   love   I have in - side   And I'll

give   it all   to   you   my   love ———————

My   end - less   love. ——————————

* For short version, finish here.

The Entertainer

Music by SCOTT JOPLIN
Adapted and Arranged
by ROGER EVANS

Piano/Guitar or Clarinet/Flute
March or Country (Medium)

Evergreen

Words by PAUL WILLIAMS
Music by BARBRA STREISAND

Flute or Jazz Organ/ Organ 2
Bossa Nova or Ballad/Pops (Medium)

Love — soft as an ea-sy chair; — love, — fresh as the morn-ing air. — One — love that is shared by two, — I have found — with you. — Like a rose — un-der the A-pril snow, — I was al-ways cer-tain love would grow. — Love, — age-less and ev-er-green, — sel-dom seen by two. —

55

Everything I Own

Words and Music
by DAVID GATES

Organ/Organ 1
Reggae or Rock (Medium)

Everything Is Beautiful

Words and Music
by RAY STEVENS

Flute/Clarinet or Vibes
Ballad/Pops or Swing (Medium)

Ev-'ry-thing is beau - ti-ful ——— in its own way, ——— Like a star-ry sum - mer night, or a snow cov-ered win——ter's day. ——— Ev-'ry-bo-dy's beau - ti-ful ——— in their own way ——— un - der God's Hea ——— ven the world's gon-na find ——— a way. —

There is none so blind ——— as
We shouldn't care about the length of his hair or the

(*If your keyboard has a 'Transposer', you could use it to change key at this point by setting it to +2, ♯2 or D.)

Every Time You Go Away

Words and Music
by DARYL HALL

Saxophone or Electric Guitar/Trumpet
Ballad/Pops (Medium-Slow)

For Once In My Life

Words by RONALD MILLER
Music by ORLANDO MURDEN

Jazz Organ
Rock (Medium)

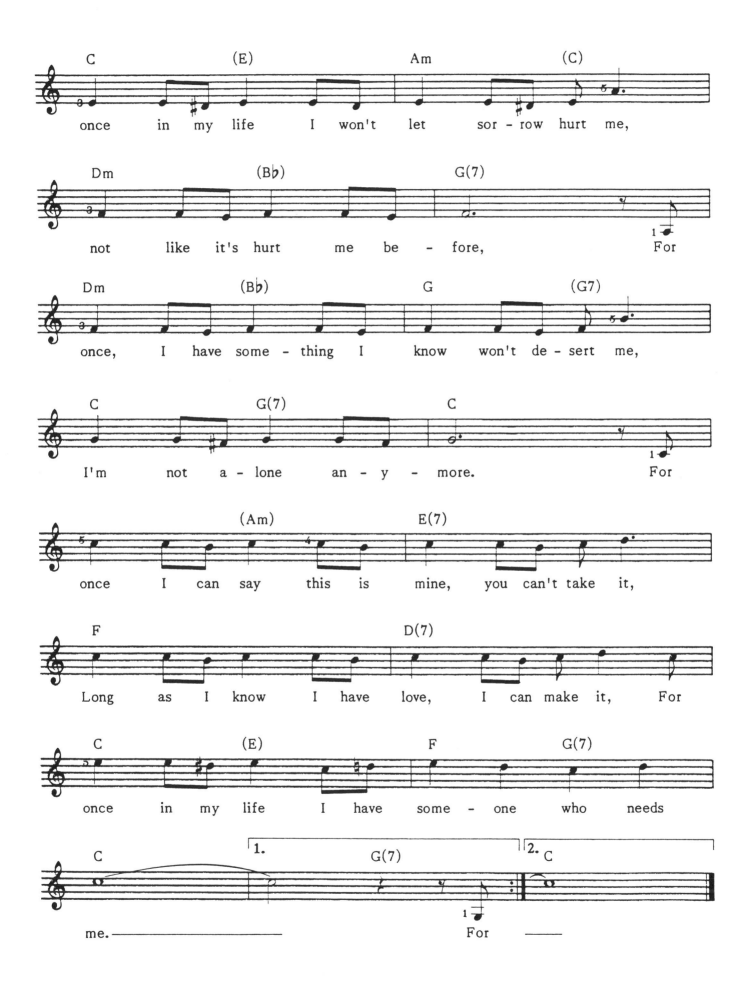

A Groovy Kind Of Love

Words and Music by
TONI WINE and CAROLE BAYER SAGER

Electric Piano/ Piano or Jazz Organ
Ballad/Pops (Medium-Slow)

When I'm feel-in' blue all I have to do is take a look at

you Then I'm not so blue when you're close to me I can feel your

heart beat I can hear you breath-ing in my ear. Would- n't you a-

gree ba - by you and me got a groo-vy kind of love

An - y-time you want to you can turn me on to an- y-thing you

want to an - y time at all. When I kiss your lips, oo, I start to

shiv - er, can't con-trol the quiv-er - ing in - side.— Would- n't you a-

(*If your keyboard has a 'Transposer', you could use it to change key at this point
by setting it to +2, ♯2, or D.)

Help Me Make It Through The Night

Words and Music
by KRIS KRISTOFFERSON

Electric Guitar/Electric Piano or Trumpet
Country or Rock (Medium)
(Add Arpeggio/Variation)

(Switch on Duet/
Counter Melody)

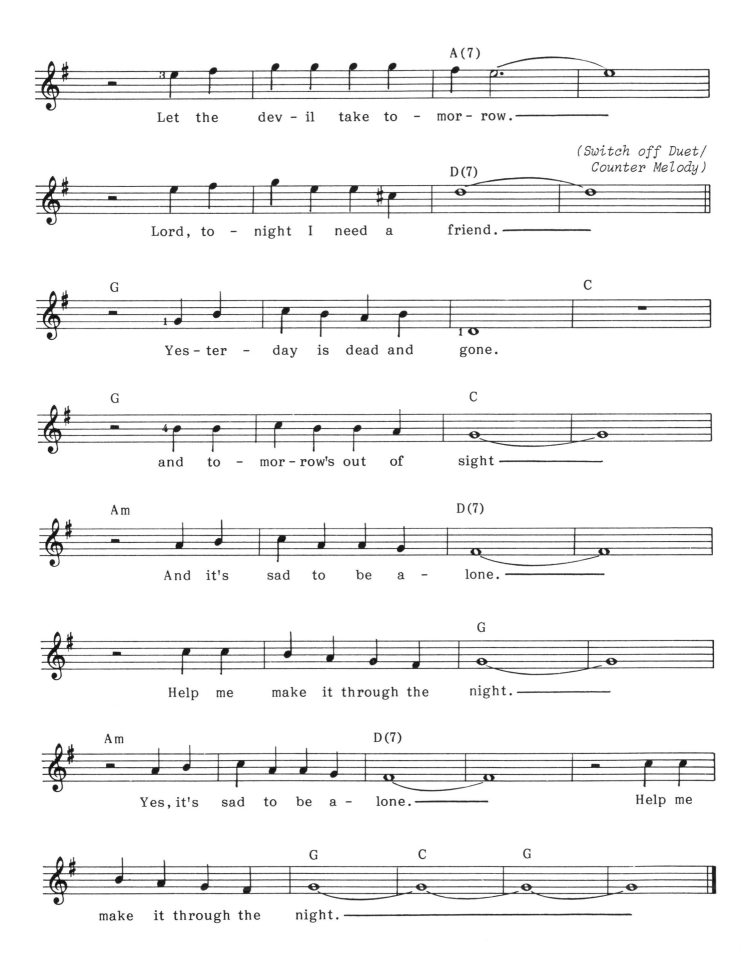

A(7)

Let the dev-il take to-mor-row.

(Switch off Duet/ Counter Melody)

D(7)

Lord, to-night I need a friend.

G   C

Yes-ter-day is dead and gone.

G   C

and to-mor-row's out of sight

Am   D(7)

And it's sad to be a-lone.

G

Help me make it through the night.

Am   D(7)

Yes, it's sad to be a-lone. Help me

G   C   G

make it through the night.

Hi Ho Silver Lining

Words and Music by
SCOTT ENGLISH and LAURENCE WEISS

Electric Guitar or Trombone/Trumpet
Rock/8-beat or Disco (Medium)

Hotel California

Words and Music by DON FELDER,
DON HENLEY and GLENN FREY

Organ or Electric Guitar
Rock/8 beat or Ballad/Pops (Medium)
(Add Arpeggio or Variation)

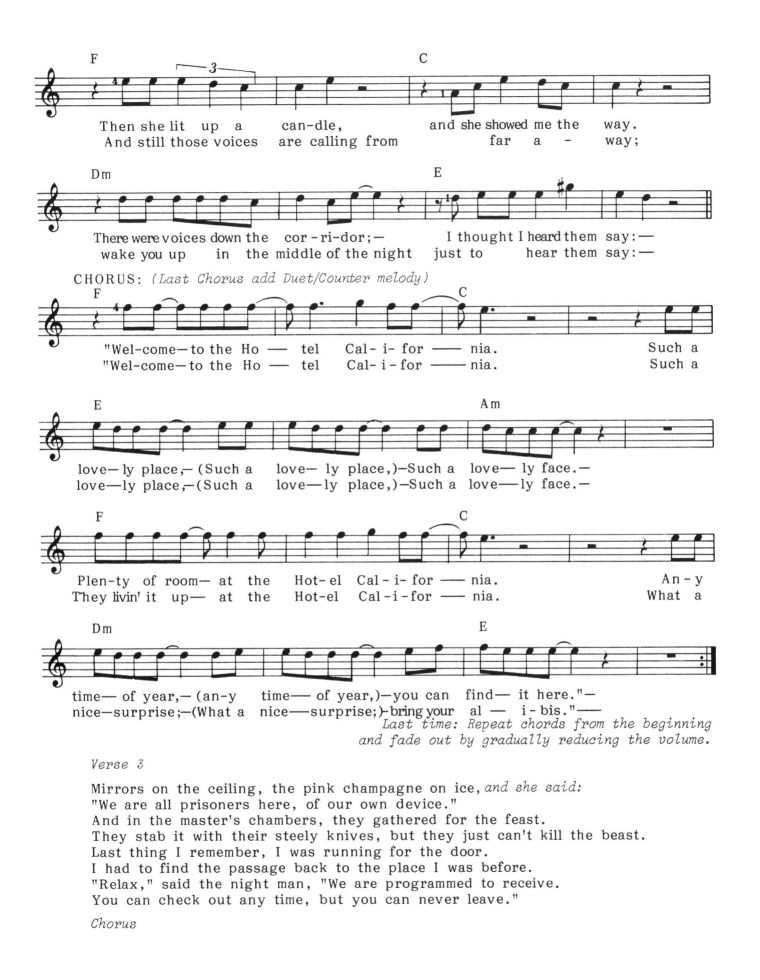

F

C

Then she lit up a can-dle, and she showed me the way.
And still those voices are calling from far a - way;

Dm

E

There were voices down the cor-ri-dor;— I thought I heard them say:—
wake you up in the middle of the night just to hear them say:—

CHORUS: *(Last Chorus add Duet/Counter melody)*

F

C

"Wel-come—to the Ho — tel Cal- i- for —— nia. Such a
"Wel-come—to the Ho — tel Cal- i-for —— nia. Such a

E

Am

love—ly place,—(Such a love— ly place,)—Such a love— ly face.—
love—ly place,—(Such a love—ly place,)—Such a love—ly face.—

F

C

Plen-ty of room— at the Hot-el Cal- i- for —— nia. An-y
They livin' it up— at the Hot-el Cal-i-for —— nia. What a

Dm

E

time— of year,— (an-y time— of year,)—you can find— it here."—
nice—surprise;—(What a nice—surprise;)—bring your al — i-bis."——

*Last time: Repeat chords from the beginning
and fade out by gradually reducing the volume.*

Verse 3

Mirrors on the ceiling, the pink champagne on ice, *and she said:*
"We are all prisoners here, of our own device."
And in the master's chambers, they gathered for the feast.
They stab it with their steely knives, but they just can't kill the beast.
Last thing I remember, I was running for the door.
I had to find the passage back to the place I was before.
"Relax," said the night man, "We are programmed to receive.
You can check out any time, but you can never leave."

Chorus

House Of The Rising Sun

Adapted and Arranged
by ROGER EVANS

Organ
Slow Rock (Medium-Slow)
(Add Arpeggio/Variation)

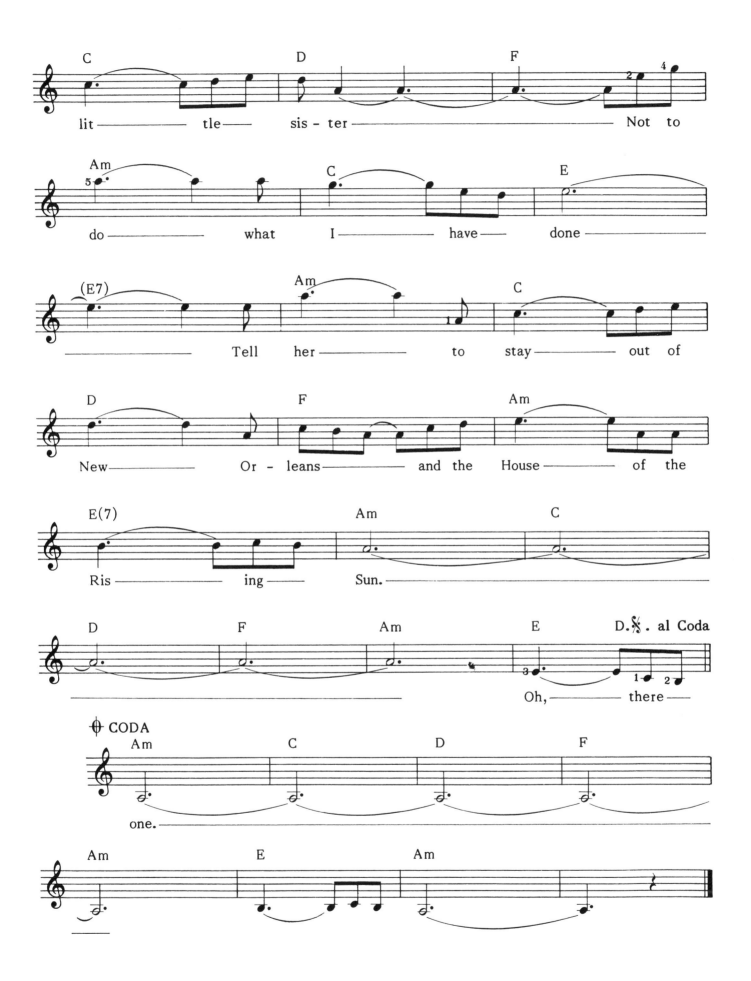

I Got You Babe

Words and Music
by SONNY BONO

Trombone/Trumpet or Jazz Organ
Reggae/Rock (Medium) – UB40 Version
Slow Rock (Medium) – Sonny & Cher

*Change Key here, from F with one flat in the key signature (B♭) to G with one sharp (F♯)

then they say your hair's too long, But   I don't care with you I can't do   wrong.   Then

put your lit-tle hand in mine   There ain't no hill or mountain we can't   climb,

babe,   I   got   you, babe   I   got   you, babe.

I   got   you   to   hold   my   hand,   I   got   you   to   un-der-stand,——

I   got   you   to   walk   with   me,   I   got   you   to   talk   with   me

I   got   you   to   kiss   good-night,   I   got   you   to   hold   me   tight,——

I   got   you,   I   won't   let   go   I   got   you   who   loves   me   so,

I   got   you,   babe.

+Switch off Synchro (with your right hand).

I Guess That's Why They Call It The Blues

Words and Music by ELTON JOHN,
BERNIE TAUPIN and DAVEY JOHNSTONE

Organ
Slow Rock (Medium)

I Heard It Through The Grapevine

Words and Music by
NORMAN WHITFIELD and **BARRETT STRONG**

Organ or Trumpet
Rock, 8-beat or Disco (Medium)

1. Mm,   I   bet you won-d'rin' how I knew
                ain't sup-posed to   cry

'Bout   your   plans   to make   me blue,——
But   these   tears   I can't hold in - side,——

With some oth - er   guy   you knew be - fore
        Los - in'   you   would end my life you see

Be - tween the two   of   us   guys you knew I loved you more——
    'Cause   you   mean   that   much to   me ——

It   took me   by   sur - prise ——————   I must
You could have   told ——————   me your-

say   When I   found   out   yes - ter - day——
- self   That you   loved ———   some - one else——

Don't you know that   I   heard   it through the grape - vine
In - stead   I   heard   it through the grape - vine

A
Not much — long - er would you be mine
Not much — long - er would you be mine
Em (A) (Em)
Heard it through the grape - vine
I heard it through the grape - vine
A
Oh, I'm just a - bout to lose — my
And, I'm just a - bout to lose — my
Em To Coda 1.
mind. mind. Hon-ey, hon- ey, oh yeah. 2. I know a man
2. D.𝄋. al Coda
Ooh. — ※ 3. Peo - ple say be-lieve half
CODA
x2
Hon - ey, hon - ey I know
(Fade)
that you're let - ting me go.

※ **Verse 3.** (People say believe half) of what you see
Son, and none of what you hear;
But I can't help but be confused
If it's true please tell me dear,
Do you plan to let me go
For the other guy you loved before.

I Only Have Eyes For You

Words by AL DUBIN
Music by HARRY WARREN

Trumpet/Brass or Jazz Organ/Organ 2
Swing (Medium - for a jazzy feeling)
or Slow Rock (Medium-Slow)

The Ice Cream Song (O Sole Mio)

Music by E. DI CAPUA
Adapted and Arranged
by ROGER EVANS

Violin/Strings
Bossa Nova (Medium)

INTRO: Backing only ————

If I Were A Rich Man

Words by SHELDON HARNICK
Music by JERRY BOCK

Clarinet/Flute or Violin/Strings
March (Medium)

It Might As Well Rain Until September

Words and Music by
GERRY GOFFIN and CAROLE KING

Flute/Clarinet or Violin/Strings
Ballad/Pops (Medium-Fast)

Lean On Me

Words and Music
by BILL WITHERS

Violin/Strings
Rock (Medium)

Light My Fire

Words and Music
by **THE DOORS**

Jazz Organ/Organ 2
Ballad/Pops (Medium-Fast)

Love Letters

Words by EDWARD HEYMAN
Music by VICTOR YOUNG

Trombone/Trumpet/Brass
Ballad/Pops (Medium Slow)

Love Of The Common People

Words and Music by
JOHN HURLEY and RONNIE WILKINS

Trombone/Trumpet or Jazz Organ
Rock or 8-beat (Medium)

Liv - in' on free food tick - ets,

Wa - ter in the milk from a hole in the roof where the rain came through.

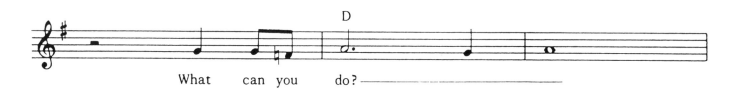

What can you do?

Tears from the lit - tle sis - ter; Cry-ing 'cause she doesn't have a

dress with-out a patch for the par - ty to go,

But you know she'll get by. 'Cause she's

liv - ing in the love of the com- mon peo — ple,

Sub-published by EMI Music Publishing Ltd, London WC2H 0EA/Westminster Music Ltd, 19/20 Poland Street, London W1V 1LB

Smiles from the heart of a fam – i – ly man.——

Dad – dy's gon – na buy you a dream to cling to,——

Ma – ma's gon – na love you just as much as she can,——

And she can.——

'Cause we're can.——

Verse 2.   It's a good thing you don't have bus fare;
It would fall through the hole in your pocket and you'd lose it in the snow on the ground.
You got to walk into town, to find a job.
Tryin' to keep your hands warm.
When the hole in your shoe lets the snow come through and chills you to the bone.
Now you'd better go home where it's warm.
Where you can live in the love . . . (Chorus)

Verse 3.   Living on a dream ain't easy,
But the closer the knit the tighter the fit and the chills stays away.
You take 'em in the stride for the family pride,
You know that faith is your foundation
And with a whole lot of love and a warm conversation, but don't forget to pray.
Making it strong where you belong,
And we're living in the love . . . (Chorus)

Mandy

Words and Music by
RICHARD KERR and SCOTT ENGLISH

Trumpet/Brass
Ballad/Pops or Bossa Nova (Medium)

I re-mem-ber all my life rain-ing down as cold as ice. Sha-dows of a man, a face through a win-dow, cry-in' in the night, the night goes in to

Morning's just an-oth-er day; hap-py peo-ple pass my way.
2. standing on the edge of time; I've walked a-way when love was

Look-ing in their eyes, I see a mem-'ry, I
mine. Caught up in a world of up-hill climb-ing, the
Yes-ter-day's a dream, I face the morn-ing.

nev-er re-a-lized how hap-py you made me.
tears are in my mind and noth-in' is rhy-ming } Oh, Man-dy, well, you
Cry-ing on a breeze the pain is call-ing:

came and you gave with-out tak-ing, But I

Dm   G(7)   C

sent you a - way.— Oh, Man —— dy, —— well, you kissed——

Am   F   G

—— me and stopped— me from sha —— king, —————— and I

G(7)   **To Coda** ⊕ C   Am

need you to-day,— Oh, Man - dy ————————————

1.   **2.**

Dm   G(7)   G(7)   **D.% al Coda**

——   **2.** I'm

⊕ **CODA**

C   Am   F

Man - dy,—— well, you came —— and you gave— with-out tak —

G   C

—— ing, but I sent—— you a - way,— Oh, Man - dy,— well, you

Am   F   G

kissed me and stopped— me from shak—— ing and I —— need ——

C   Am   G   C

you.————————————————————

Mexican Hat Dance

Adapted and Arranged
by ROGER EVANS

Trumpet/Brass or Violin/Strings
Waltz (Medium-Fast)
(Add Duet/Counter Melody/Auto Harmonize)

Misty

Words by JOHNNY BURKE
Music by ERROLL GARNER

Jazz Organ/Organ 2 or Trumpet
Ballad/Pops (Slow)

Look at me, I'm as help-less as a kit-ten up a tree And I feel like I'm cling-ing to a cloud, I can't un-der-stand I get mist-y just hold-ing your hand. Walk my way and a thou-sand vi-o-lins be-gin to play, Or it might be the sound of your hel-lo, That mu-sic I hear I get mist-y, the mo-ment you're

Moonlight (Clair de Lune)

Music by CLAUDE DEBUSSY
New Arrangement
by ROGER EVANS

Organ/Flute or Vibes
Slow Rock or 6-beat (Slow) or play with rhythm switched off
(Add Arpeggio/Variation)

Moon River

Words by JOHNNY MERCER
Music by HENRY MANCINI

Violin/Strings or Trumpet
Waltz (Slow)
(Add Variation)

The More I See You

Words by MACK GORDON
Music by HARRY WARREN

Organ/Organ 1
Ballad/Pops or Bossa Nova (Medium-Fast)

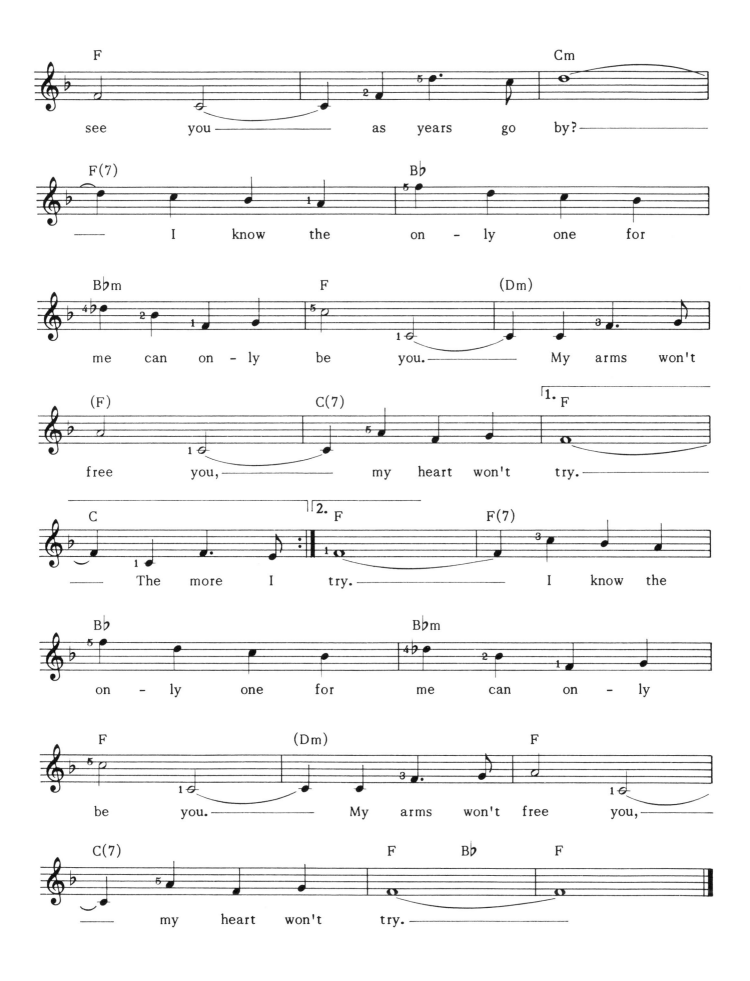

Mr. Tambourine Man

Words and Music
by BOB DYLAN

Organ
Ballad/Pops (Medium-Fast)
(Add Arpeggio/Variation)

Hey! Mist - er Tam - bour - ine Man play a song for me, I'm not sleep-y and there is no place I'm go - in' to. _____ Hey! Mist - er Tam - bour - ine Man play a song for me in the jin - gle jan - gle morn - in' I'll come fol _____ low-in' you. _____

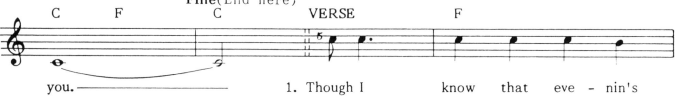

1. Though I know that eve - nin's

em - pire has re - turned in - to sand,

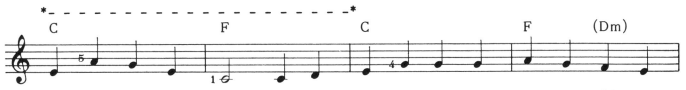

Van-ished from my hand, Left me blind-ly here to stand but still not

sleep-in'.———————— My wear-i-ness a-ma-zes me I'm

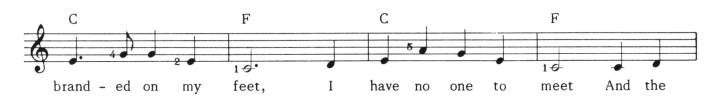

brand-ed on my feet, I have no one to meet And the

an-cient emp-ty street's too dead for dreamin'.————

- - - - Repeat these bars to fit in extra lyrics for verses 2, 3 & 4.

Verse 3. Take me on a trip upon your magic swirlin' ship
My senses have been stripped, my hands can't feel to grip,
My toes too numb to step, wait only for my boot heels to be wanderin'.
I'm ready to go anywhere, I'm ready for to fade
Into my own parade, cast your dancin' spell my way
I promise to go under it.

Verse 3. Though you might hear laughin' spinnin' swingin' madly across the sun
It's not aimed at anyone, it's just escapin' on the run
And but for the sky there are no fences facin'.
And if you hear vague traces, of skippin' reels of rhyme
To your tambourine in time, it's just a ragged clown behind,
I wouldn't pay it any mind, it's just a shadow
You're seein' that he's chasin'.

Verse 4. Then take me disappearin' through the smoke rings of my mind
Down the foggy ruins of time, far past the frozen leaves,
The haunted frightened trees, out to the windy beach
Far from the twisted reach of crazy sorrow.
Yes, to dance beneath the diamond sky, with one hand wavin' free
Silhouetted by the sea, circled by the circus sands
With all memory and fate, driven deep beneath the waves.
Let me forget about today until tomorrow.

Repeat refrain.

My Way

French Words by GILLES THIBAUT
English Lyrics by PAUL ANKA
Music by CLAUDE FRANCOIS and JACQUES REVAUX

Trumpet/Brass or Organ
Ballad/Pops or Swing (Medium-Slow)

Never Can Say Goodbye

Words and Music
by CLIFTON DAVIS

Violin/Strings
Disco or Rock (Medium)

Nev-er can say good-bye no, no, no, no, I

nev-er can say good-bye.

Verse

1. E - ven
2. Ev - 'ry

though the pain and heart-ache seem to fol-low me wherever I go;— Though I
time I think I've had e - nough and start head - ing for the door,— There's

tried and tried to hide my feel-ings they al-ways seem to show, Then you
ve - ry strange vi - bra-tions, pierc - ing me right to the core. It says

try to say you're leav-ing me and I al-ways have to say no, tell me
turn a-round you fool——— you know you love her more and more, tell me

1. why is it so? But I—

2. why is it so? Don't wan - na let you

Verse 3. (I keep) thinkin' that our problems soon are all gonna work out,
But there's that same unhappy feelin', there's that anguish, there's that doubt.
It's the same old dizzy hang-up, can't do with you or without.
Tell me why, is it so? Don't wanna let you go.

Nights In White Satin

Words and Music
by JUSTIN HAYWARD

Organ/Organ 1 (Optional: Change to Flute later)
Slow Rock or 6-beat (Slow)
(Add Stereo Chorus/Stereo Symphonic)

Night-Time In Moscow

Adapted and Arranged
by ROGER EVANS

Trumpet/Trombone or Clarinet
Swing (Medium Fast)

* Key change to Am, Play B (♮) instead of B♭ from here on.

117

Nobody Does It Better

Words by CAROLE BAYER SAGER
Music by MARVIN HAMLISCH

Flute or Organ
Ballad/Pops (Medium-Slow)

1. No - bo - dy does   it   bet - ter———
2. No - bo - dy does   it   bet - ter———

makes me feel sad   for the   rest,
some-times I wish   some - one   could,

No - bo - dy does   it   half   as good as you.
No - bo - dy does   it   quite   the way you do.

Ba - by, you're the   best.
Did you have to be so   good?

I was-n't look - in'   but some-how you found me.
The way that you hold   me   when-ev - er you hold me.

I tried to hide from   your   love   light,
There's some kind of mag - ic   in - side   you

But like hea-ven a-bove me   the spy who loved me   is
That keeps me from run-nin'   but just keep it com - in'———

O Danny Boy

Adapted and Arranged
by ROGER EVANS

Organ or Flute
Ballad/Pops (Medium)
(Arpeggio/Variation)

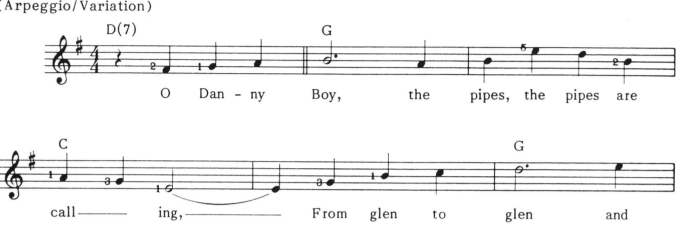

O Dan - ny Boy, the pipes, the pipes are

call———ing,——— From glen to glen and

o'er the moun-tain side.——————— The sum-mer's gone, and

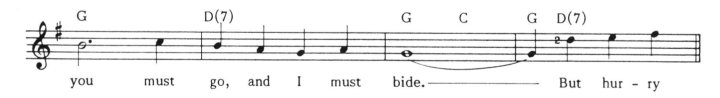

all the leaves are fall———ing,——— It's you, it's

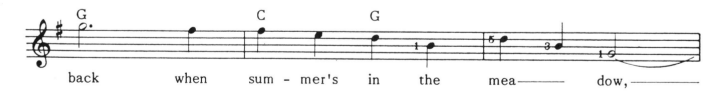

you must go, and I must bide.——————— But hur - ry

back when sum - mer's in the mea———dow,———

——— or when the val - ley's hushed and white with snow,———

One Moment In Time

Words and Music by
ALBERT HAMMOND and JOHN BETTIS

Violin/Strings or Organ
Ballad/Pops (Medium)

Each day I live I want to be a day to

give the best of me. I'm on-ly one but not a-

-lone, my fin-est day is yet un-known. I broke my

heart for ev-'ry gain, to taste the sweet I faced the
be the ve-ry best, I want it all, no time for

pain, I rise and fall yet through it all this much re-
less, I've laid the plans, now lay the chance here in my

-mains. I want one mo-ment in time When I'm
hands. Give me

Dm   G   F   G
more than I thought I could be. When all of my dreams are a

Over The Rainbow

Words by E Y HARBURG
Music by HAROLD ARLEN

Trumpet/Brass or Jazz Organ
Ballad/Pops (Medium-Slow)

Over The Waves

Music by JUVENTINO ROSAS
Adapted and Arranged
by ROGER EVANS

Flute or Clarinet
Waltz (Medium)
(Add Variation)

D.C. al Fine
(Returning to beginning and play to 'Fine')

Paloma Blanca

Words and Music
by J BOUWENS

Trumpet/Brass or Clarinet
March or Country (Medium-Fast)

*Instrumental (Optional)**

——— When the sun shines on the moun - tains ———

——— And the night is on the run ———

——— It's a new day, It's a new way ———

——— And I fly up to the sun. *Instrumental** ———

I can feel the
had my

morn - ing sun - light, ——— I can smell the new-mown
share of los - ing, ——— For they locked me on a

129

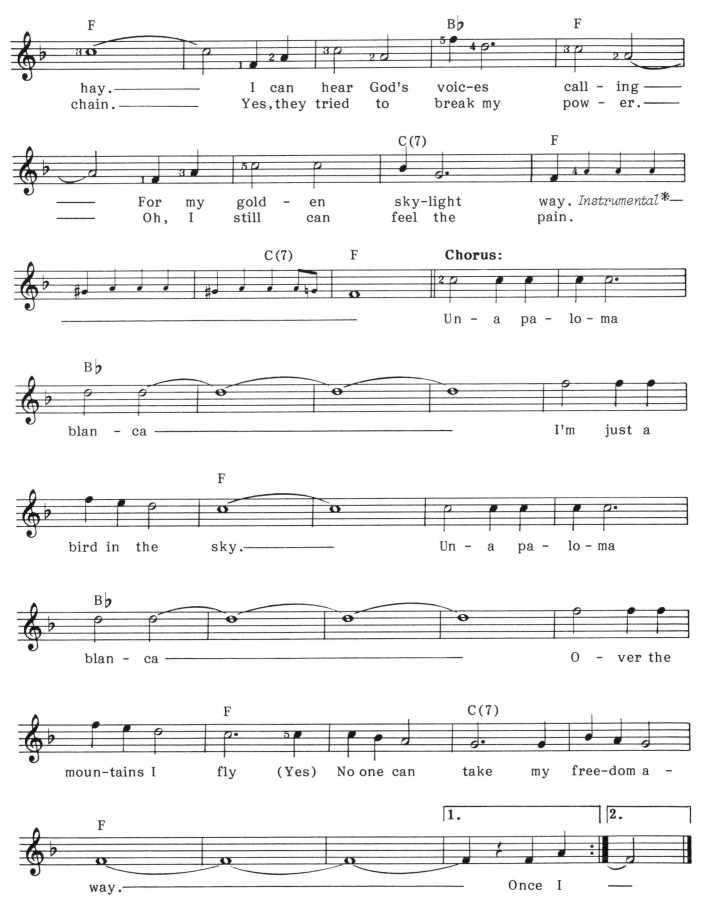

All Instrumental breaks are optional and may be left out if you wish.

Piano In The Dark

Words and Music by BRENDA RUSSELL,
JEFF HULL and SCOTT CUTLER

Flute or Electric Piano/Piano*
Bossa Nova or Ballad/Pops (Medium)
(*Add Stereo Chorus/Stereo Symphonic)

When I find my-self watch-in' the time, -

I nev-er think a-bout all the fun-ny things you've

said; ——— I feel like it's dead.— The feel-ings in me now

I turn a-round in the still of the room
He holds me close like a beat of a heart.

Know-ing this is when I'm gon-na make my move.— Can't
He plays the mel-o-dy, want to tear me all a-part.—— The

wait an-y long-er and I'm feel-ing strong-er,But oh, just as I
si-lence is bro-ken and no words are spo-ken.

walk to the door I can feel your e - mo - tion

Remember The Night (Danube Waves)

Music by JAN IVANOVICI
Adapted and Arranged
by ROGER EVANS

Flute/Clarinet or Trumpet
Waltz (Medium-Fast) or Slow Rock
(Add Arpeggio/Variation)

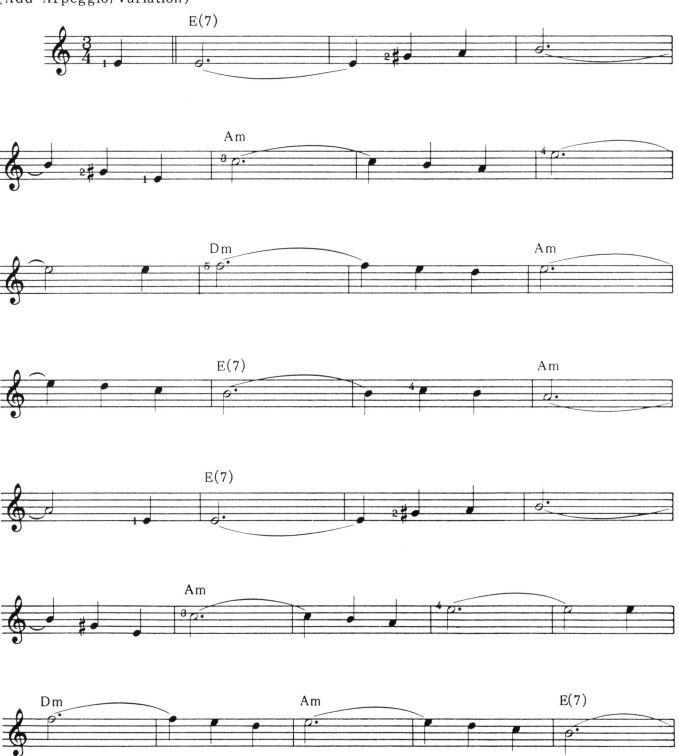

Satisfaction (I Can't Get No)

Words by Music by
MICK JAGGER and KEITH RICHARDS

Jazz Organ/Organ 2 or Violin/Strings
8-beat, Rock or Disco (Medium-Fast)

Saving All My Love For You

Words by GERRY GOFFIN
Music by MICHAEL MASSER

Violin/Strings or Organ
Slow Rock (Medium-Slow)

got to get read-y, just a few minutes more. Gonna get that old feeling when you

walk through the door, 'Cause to - night is the night for— feel - ing all right. We'll be

mak-ing love the whole night— through, so I'm sav-ing all my love, yes I'm

sav - ing all my love, yes I'm sav-ing all my love for— you.—

——— No oth - er wo-man is gon - na love you more, 'Cause to -

- night is the night that I'm feel - ing all right, We'll be making love the whole night—

through;— so I'm sav-ing all my love, yes I'm sav-ing all my lov-ing, yes I'm

sav - ing all my love for you.—

Secret Love

Words by PAUL FRANCIS WEBSTER
Music by SAMMY FAIN

Violin/Strings 50
Slow Rock or Swing (Medium) b4 BB Ballad
Tempo 99

Once I had a se - cret love

That lived with - in the heart of me, All too

soon that se - cret love Be -

- came im - pa - tient to be free,

So I told a friend - ly star,

The way that dream - ers oft - en

Skye Boat Song

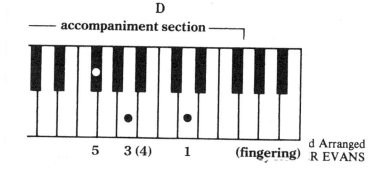

accompaniment section

D

5   3 (4)   1   **(fingering)**

d Arranged
R EVANS

Flute/Clarinet or Accordion
Waltz (Medium-Slow)
(Add Arpeggio/Variation)

"Speed bon-nie boat, like a bird on the wing, On - ward!" the sail - ors cry. "Car - ry the lad that's born to be King, O - ver the sea to Skye."

Loud the winds howl, loud the waves roar, Thun - der clouds rend the

Smoke Gets In Your Eyes

Words by OTTO HARBACH
Music by JEROME KERN

Trumpet (Change to Violin or Strings later)
Ballad/Pops (Medium–Not too fast)

So I chaffed——— them and I gai - ly laughed——— to think they could

doubt my love.

Yet to-day——— My love has flown a - way,——— I am with -

- out my love. *(Change back to Trumpet)*

Now laugh - ing friends de - ride Tears I can - not

hide,——— So I smile and

say, "When a love-ly flame dies, Smoke gets in your

eyes."———

Snowbird

Words and Music
by GENE MacLELLAN

Flute/Clarinet or Violin Strings
Ballad/Pops (Medium-Fast)

Spanish Eyes

Words by CHARLES SINGLETON and EDDIE SNYDER
Music by BERT KAEMPFERT

Trumpet/Brass
Bossa Nova (Medium)
(Second time through add Duet/Counter Melody)

Stairway To Heaven

Words and Music by
JIMMY PAGE and ROBERT PLANT

Jazz Organ/Organ 2 or Flute
8-beat or Rock (Slow)
(Add Arpeggio/Variation)

150

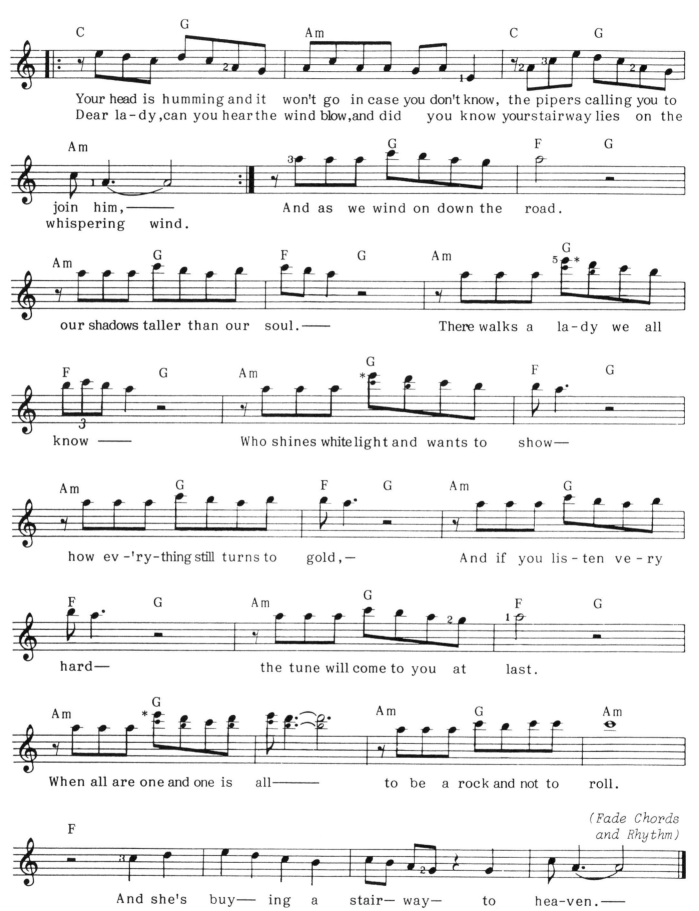

Your head is humming and it won't go in case you don't know, the pipers calling you to
Dear la-dy, can you hear the wind blow, and did you know your stairway lies on the

join him,——— And as we wind on down the road.
whispering wind.

our shadows taller than our soul.—— There walks a la-dy we all

know ——— Who shines white light and wants to show—

how ev -'ry-thing still turns to gold,— And if you lis-ten ve-ry

hard— the tune will come to you at last.

(Fade Chords
and Rhythm)

When all are one and one is all——— to be a rock and not to roll.

And she's buy—ing a stair—way— to hea-ven.——

(* If you cannot play the high E or D on your keyboard, play the small notes instead.)

Sloop John B

Adapted and Arranged
by ROGER EVANS

Trumpet/Brass or Vibes
Bossa Nova (Medium)

1. We came on the Sloop John B, My old grand dad-dy and
   hoist up the John B sails See how the main sail's

me, All a-round Nas-sau Town We — did roam.
set, Send for the Captain a - shore Let me go home.

— Drinking all night — Got in a fight, — I
— Let me go home — Let me go home, — I

feel so broke up, I want to go home.
feel so broke up, I want to go home. Chorus: So

Last time only

I feel so broke up, I want to go home. —

Verse 2.   The first mate he got drunk
Broke up the people's trunk
Constable had to come and take him away.
Sheriff John Stone, please leave me alone
I feel so broke up I want to go home.

Chorus.

Verse 3.   The cook he got the fits,
He ate up all of my grits.
Then he took and ate up all of my corn
Leave me alone, I want to go home,
This is the worst trip I've ever been on.

Chorus.

Stay With Me (Jazz Samba)

Music by ROGER EVANS

Trombone/Trumpet or Saxophone
Samba (Medium)
(Add Variation)

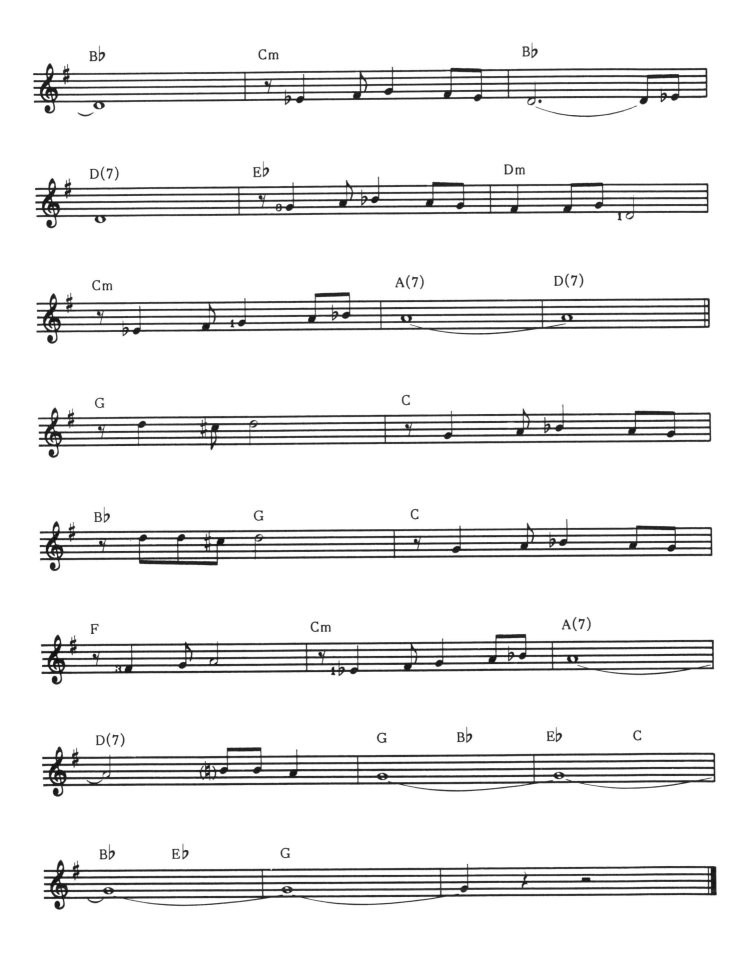

The Summer Knows (Theme From 'Summer Of 42')

Words by MARILYN and ALAN BERGMAN
Music by MICHEL LEGRAND

Piano/Electric Piano or Violin/Strings
Ballad/Pops (Slow)
(Add Arpeggio or Variation)

moon   to   wait   and the   sun   to   lin - ger,

Twists   the   world   'round her   sum - mer   fin - ger,

Lets   you   see   the   won - der   of   it   all,   And

if you've learned——your   les-son well,   There's lit - tle more——— for

*(Key Change)

her   to   tell,   One   last   car - ess,——————— it's

1. time   to   dress   for   fall.——————————   The

2. fall.———————————   (Instrumental ——————————)

* **Note:** This music changes key from G minor with two flats (B♭ and E♭) in the key signature, to G (major) with one sharp (F♯) in the key signature. Then it changes back again to G minor.

Summertime

Words by DuBOSE HEYWARD
Music by GEORGE GERSHWIN

Flute or Clarinet
Bossa Nova (Medium)
(Add Stereo Chorus or Stereo Symphonic)

Sum - mer - time ——————— an' the liv-in' is eas - y, ——— Fish are jump-in' ——— an' the cotton is high. ——————— Oh, your dad-dy's rich — an' your ma is good look - in', ——— So hush lit-tle ba - by, don' — you cry. ——— One of these morn - in's you goin' to rise — up

Swinging On A Star

Words by JOHNNY BURKE
Music by JIMMY VAN HEUSEN

Trombone/Trumpet or Clarinet
Ballad/Pops or Swing (Medium)

(See next page for optional "intro")

1. A mule is an an - i - mal with long fun - ny ears, He kicks up at an - y - thing he hears. His back is brawn - y but his brain is weak, He's just plain stu - pid with a stub - born streak, And by the way if you hate to go to school, Or would you like to swing on a mule.

pig is an an - i - mal with dirt on his face, His shoes are a ter - ri - ble dis - grace. He's got no man - ners when he eats his food, He's just fat and la - zy and ex - treme - ly rude, But if you don't care a fea - ther or a fig, Or would you like to swing on a pig.

fish won't do an - y - thing but swim in a brook, He can't write his name or read a book. To fool the peo - ple is his on - ly thought, And though he's slip - per - y, he still gets caught, But then if that sort of life is what you wish, And all the mon - keys aren't in the fish.

*Hold down note and change fingers

*Hold down note and change fingers

Take Good Care Of My Baby

Words and Music by
GERRY GOFFIN and CAROLE KING

Electric Piano or Trumpet/Brass
Ballad/Pops or Rock (Medium-Fast)

Tell It To My Heart

Words and Music by
ERNIE GOLD and SETH SWIRSKY

Trumpet/Brass
Disco (Medium-Fast)

Instrumental

I feel the
The pas - sion

night ex - plode —— when we're to-geth - er.
so com - plete —— it's nev - er end - ing.

E - mo - tion o - ver-load—— in the heat of
As long as I re - ceive—— the mess - age

plea-sure. Take me I'm yours, in - to your arms,
you're sending. Body to your bo - dy, soul to soul,

nev - er let me go. To - night I
al - ways feel you near, So say the

real - ly need to know. ——
words I long to hear. —— Tell it to my

163

There's A Kind Of Hush

Words and Music by
LES REED and GEOFF STEPHENS

Piano/Electric Guitar or Jazz Organ
Ballad/Pops (Medium-Fast)

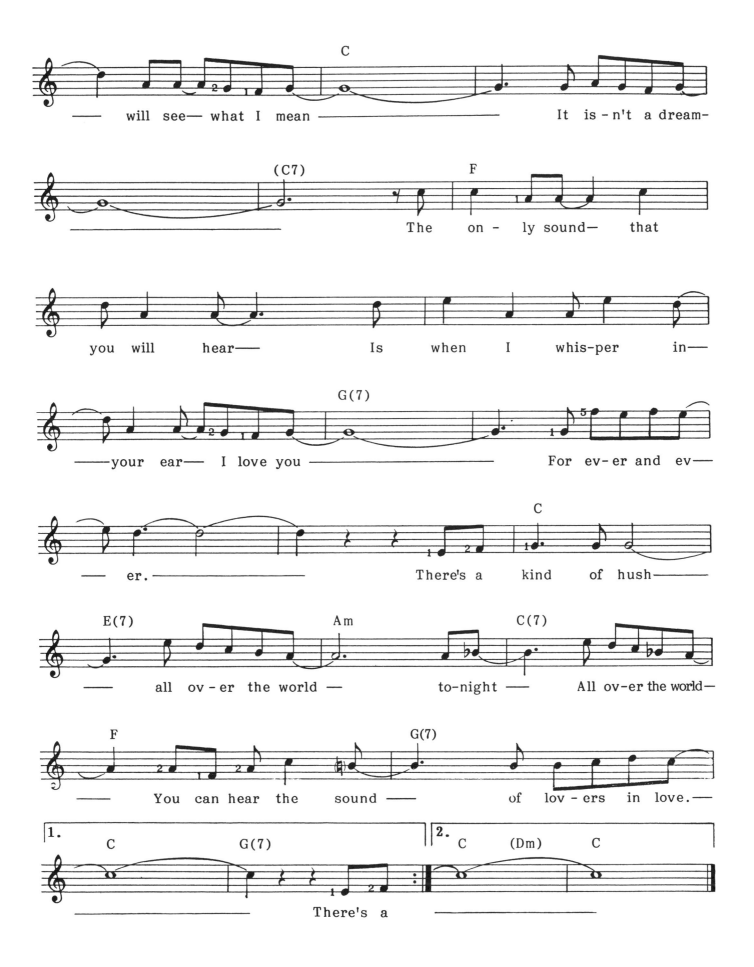

Tonight I Celebrate My Love

Words and Music by
MICHAEL MASSER and GERRY GOFFIN

Flute/Clarinet
Ballad/Pops (Slow)
(Add Arpeggio/Variation)

The Tracks Of My Tears

Words and Music by WILLIAM "SMOKEY" ROBINSON,
WARREN MOORE and MARV TARPLIN

Organ or Trumpet
Rock or Ballad/Pops (Medium-Not too fast)

tears.
tears.
Oh——————— I need
I need

you
you
need——————— you.
need——————— you.

My smile is my make - up I

wear since my break - up with you. Ba - by, take a

good look at my face——————— you'll see my

smile——————— looks out of place.——————— If you look

clo - ser it's ea - sy to trace the tracks of my

tears, Oh.———————

True Love

Words and Music by COLE PORTER

Violin/Strings or Clarinet/Flute
Waltz (Slow)
(Add Arpeggio/Variation)

Try To Remember

Words by **TOM JONES**
Music by **HARVEY SCHMIDT**

Up Where We Belong

Words by WILL JENNINGS
Music by BUFFY SAINTE-MARIE and JACK NITZSCHE

Trumpet/Brass
Ballad/Pops (Medium)

(* If your keyboard has a 'Transposer,' you could use it to change Key at this point by setting it to +1 or C♯.)

We'll Meet Again

Words and Music by
ROSS PARKER and HUGHIE CHARLES

Trombone/Trumpet/Brass
Swing or Slow Rock (Medium)

What A Wonderful World

Words and Music by
GEORGE DAVID WEISS and BOB THIELE

Trumpet/Brass
Ballad/Pops or Slow Rock (Medium)

What's Love Got To Do With It

Words and Music by
GRAHAM LYLE and TERRY BRITTEN

Jazz Organ/Organ 2 or Saxophone
Rock (Medium)

When I Need You

Words by CAROLE BAYER SAGER
Music by ALBERT HAMMOND

Violin/Strings
Waltz (Medium)

When I need you, — I just close my
eyes and I'm with you — And all that I
so wan-na give you, — It's on-ly a
heart - beat a - way. — When I

need love, — I hold out my hands and I
need you, — I just close my eyes and I'm
touch love. — I nev-er knew there was so
with you — And all that I so wan - na

much love Keep - ing me warm night and
give you, It's on - ly a heart - beat a -

C

day.

To Coda ⊕ Dm

Miles and miles of emp - ty
It's not ea - sy when the

C

space in be - tween us;
road is your dri - ver.

The

Dm

tel - e-phone can't take the place of your smile
Hon - ey, that's a hea - vy load that we bear

C

C(7)

But you know I won't be tra - vel - ing for
But you know I won't be tra - vel - ing a

F   Dm

Gm

ev - er.
life - time.

It's cold out, But

C(7)

1.

hold out, And do like I do. When I

2.   F   C(7)   D. 𝄋. al Coda

do, Oh, I need you. When I

⊕ CODA (C7)   F   B♭   F

Oh, I need you.

Where Do I Begin (Theme from 'Love Story')

Words by CARL SIGMAN
Music by FRANCIS LAI

Piano (Change to Violin or Strings later)
Bossa Nova (Medium) 96
(Add Stereo Chorus/Stereo Symphonic)

Where do I be-gin ——— to tell the sto-ry of how
How long does it last? ——— Can love be mea-sured by the

great a love can be, ——— The sweet love sto-ry that is
ho-urs in a day? ——— I have no an-swers now, but

old-er than the sea, ——— The sim-ple truth a-bout the
this much I can say: ——— I know I'll need her 'til the

To Coda

love she brings to me? ———
stars all burn a-way ——— Where do I

(Change to Violin or Strings)

start? ———

With her first hel-lo ——— she gave a mean-ing to this

emp-ty world of mine; ——— There'd nev-er be an-oth-er

A Whiter Shade Of Pale

Words and Music by
KEITH REID and **GARY BROOKER**

Organ/Organ 1
8-beat or Ballad/Pops (Medium-Slow)

We skipped the light fan - dan - go ——
She said, "There is no rea - son, ——

—— And turned cartwheels cross the floor.——
—— And the truth is plain to see," ——

——————— I was feel - ing kind of sea - sick ——
——————— But I wan-dered through my playing cards ——

—— But the crowd called— out for more.——
—— And would not— let her be.——

Will You Love Me Tomorrow

Words and Music by
GERRY GOFFIN and CAROLE KING

Organ or Flute/Clarinet
Rock or Ballad/Pops (Medium)

The Wind Beneath My Wings

Words and Music by
LARRY HENLY and JEFF SILBAR

Violin/Strings or Jazz Organ
Ballad/Pops (Medium-Slow)
(Add Arpeggio/Variation)

1. It must have been cold there in my sha - dow,
2. I was the one with all the glor - y,

to nev-er have sun-light —— on your face.
while you were the one with —— all the strength.

You've been con - tent to let me shine,
On-ly a face with-out a name.

you al - ways walked one step be -
I nev - er once heard you com -

- hind.
- plain.

Did you ev - er know that you're my he - ro,

and ev-'ry - thing I'd like to be?

You Don't Have To Say You Love Me

Original Italian Words by V PALLAVICINI
English Lyrics by VICKI WICKHAM and SIMON NAPIER-BELL
Music by P DONAGGIO

Trumpet/Brass or Jazz Organ
Slow Rock (Medium-Slow)

You Light Up My Life

Words and Music
by JOE BROOKS

Violin/Strings or Jazz Organ/Organ 2
Waltz (Medium-Slow)
(Add Arpeggio/Variation)

So man - y nights I'd sit by my
Roll - in' at sea, a - drift on the

win - dow wait - ing for some - one to sing me his
wa - ters, could it be fin - 'lly I'm turn - ing for

song. So man - y dreams I kept deep in -
home. Fin - 'lly a chance to say, "Hey I

- side me, a - lone in the dark, but now
love you." Nev - er a - gain to

you've come a - long. And you light up my
be all a - lone.

life. You give me hope, to car - ry

on. You light up my days and fill my

You Needed Me

Words and Music
by RANDY GOODRUM

Trumpet/Brass or Electric Guitar
Ballad/Pops (Medium-Slow)

1. I cried a tear, — you wiped it dry. — I was con - fused, — you cleared my mind. — I sold my soul, — you bought it back for me — and held me up — and gave me dig - ni - ty. — Some-how you need- ed me.

2. (You held my) hand — when it was cold. — When I was lost, — you took me home. — You gave me hope, — when I was at the end, — and turned my lies — back in - to truth a - gain. — You ev - en called me 'friend'.

You gave me strength — to stand a - lone a - gain — to face the world — out on my own a - gain. — You put me

You To Me Are Everything

Words and Music by
KEN GOLD and MICHAEL DENNE

Jazz Organ/Organ 2 or Flute
Rock or Disco (Medium)

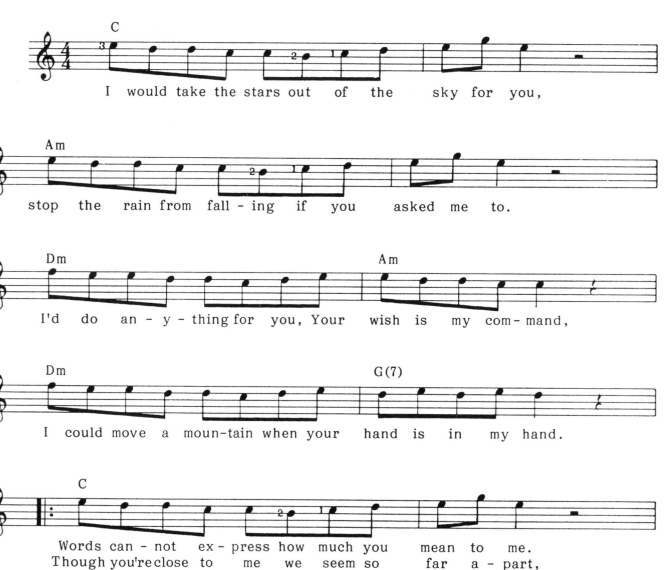

I would take the stars out of the sky for you,

stop the rain from fall-ing if you asked me to.

I'd do an-y-thing for you, Your wish is my com-mand,

I could move a moun-tain when your hand is in my hand.

Words can-not ex-press how much you mean to me.
Though you're close to me we seem so far a-part,

There must be some oth-er way to make you see. If it takes my heart and soul you
May-be, giv-en time, you'll have a change of heart. If it takes for-ev-er, girl, then

know I'd pay the price. Ev-'ry-thing that I poss-ess I'd glad-ly sac-ri-fice. Oh
I'm prepared to wait. The day you give your love to me won't be a day too late.

You'll Never Walk Alone

Words by OSCAR HAMMERSTEIN II
Music by RICHARD RODGERS

Violin/Strings
Ballad/Pops (Medium)

201

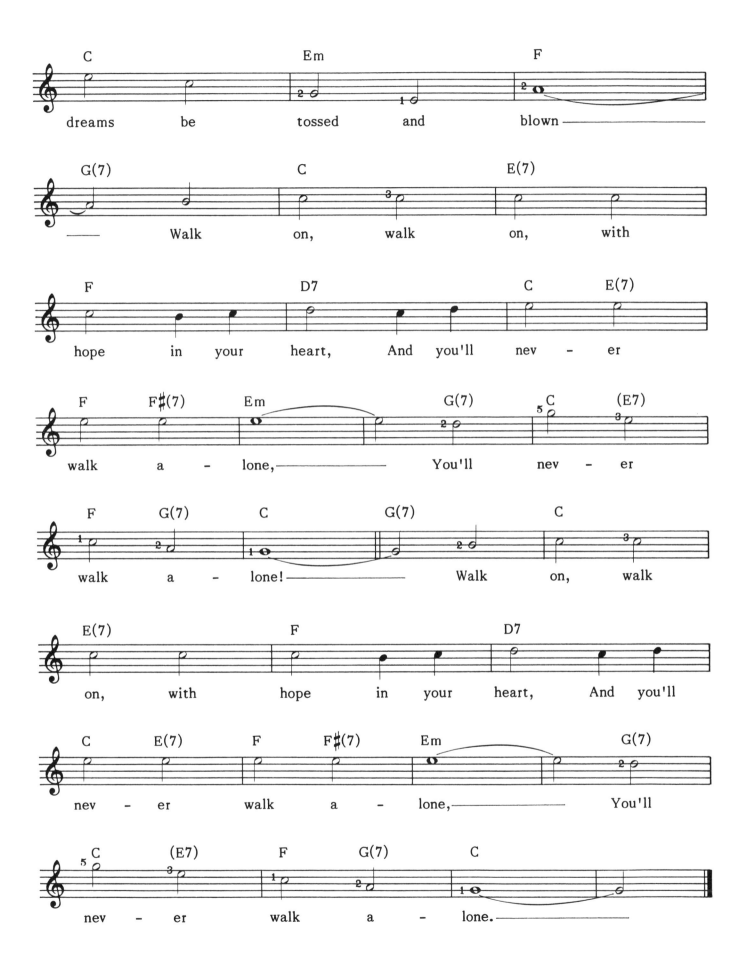

You're So Vain

Words and Music
by CARLY SIMON

Jazz Organ/Organ 2 or Electric Guitar
Ballad/Pops (Medium/Medium-Fast)

203

You've Lost That Lovin' Feelin'

Words and Music by PHIL SPECTOR,
BARRY MANN and CYNTHIA WEIL

Organ or Violin/Strings
Ballad/Pops (Medium-Slow)

gone, Woh oh oh oh. 2. Now there's no

oh. *(Instrumental* ∗ ———————————— *)* Ba – by, ba – by, I'd get

down on my knees for you. *(Instrumental* ———————————— *)*

If that would make you love me like you used to do. *(Instrumental* —

———————————— *)* We had a love, a love you don't find ev – er – y

day. *(Instrumental* ———————————— *)* So don't, don't

don't, don't let it slip a – way. ————————————

oh. *(Instrumental* ———————————— *)*

∗ *All Instrumentals optional*

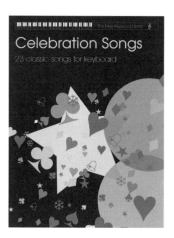

The Easy Keyboard Library

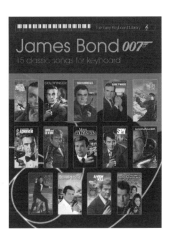

Favourite Hymns

The Fifties

Film Classics

The Forties

Frank Sinatra

George & Ira Gershwin

George Michael

Gilbert & Sullivan

Glenn Miller

Great Songwriters

I Try & 10 More Chart Hits

Instrumental Classics

James Bond

Jazz Classics

Latin Collection

Love Songs Vol 1

Love Songs Vol 2

Motown Classics

Music Hall

Nat King Cole

The Nineties

No.1 Hits Vol 1

No.1 Hits Vol 2

Popular Classics

Pub Singalong Collection

Queen

The Easy Keyboard Library

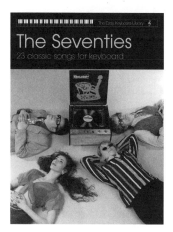

Rock 'n' Roll Classics

Scott Joplin

The Seventies

Shirley Bassey

Showtunes Vol 1

Showtunes Vol 2

The Sixties

Soft Rock Collection

Soul Classics

The Thirties

Traditional Irish Favourites

TV Themes

The Twenties

Wartime Collection

Wedding Collection

Whitney Houston

FABER ff MUSIC

To buy Faber Music publications or to find out about the full range of titles available
please contact your local music retailer or Faber Music sales enquiries:

Faber Music Ltd, Burnt Mill, Elizabeth Way, Harlow CM20 2HX
Tel: +44 (0) 1279 82 89 82   Fax: +44 (0) 1279 82 89 83
sales@fabermusic.com   fabermusic.com